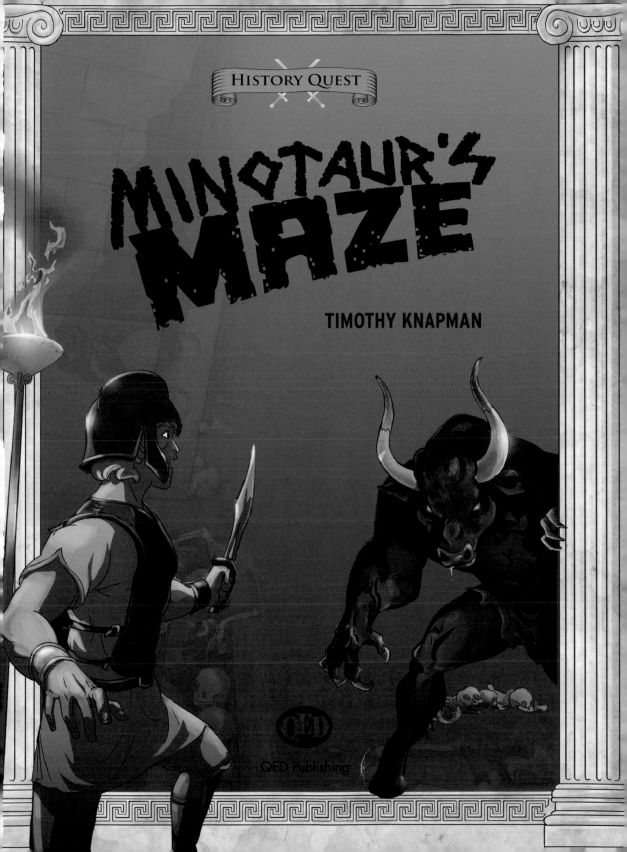

HISTORY QUEST

MINOTAUR'S MAZE

TIMOTHY KNAPMAN

QED Publishing

Cover Design: Punch Bowl Design
Illustrator: Matteo Pincelli
Editor: Amanda Askew
Designer: Andrew Crowson

QED Project Editor: Ruth Symons
Managing Editor: Victoria Garrard
Design Manager: Anna Lubecka

First published in the UK in 2013 by
QED Publishing
A Quarto Group company
230 City Road
London EC1V 2TT

www.qed-publishing.co.uk

A catalogue record for this book is available
from the British Library.

ISBN 978 1 78171 148 4

Printed in China

Picture credits
Shutterstock: Antipathique, 28; Elm, 8; Yiannis
Papadimitriou, 20;

How to begin your adventure

Are you ready for an amazing adventure in which you must face deadly foes, survive terrible dangers and solve fiendish puzzles? Then you've come to the right place!

Minotaur's Maze isn't an ordinary book – you don't read the pages in order, 1, 2, 3... Instead you jump forwards and backwards through the book as you face a series of challenges. Sometimes you may lose your way, but the story will always guide you back to where you need to be.

The story begins on page 4, where there are questions to answer and puzzles to solve. Choose which answer you think is correct. For example:

IF YOU THINK THE CORRECT ANSWER IS A, GO TO PAGE 37

IF YOU THINK THE CORRECT ANSWER IS B, GO TO PAGE 13

If you think the correct answer is A, turn to page 37 and look for the same symbol in blue. That's where you will find the next part of the story.

If you make the wrong choice, the text will explain where you went wrong and let you have another go.

The problems in this book are about life in ancient Greece. To solve them, you must use your historical knowledge, as well as common sense. To help you, there's a glossary of useful words at the back of the book, starting on page 44.

Are you ready?
Turn the page and let your adventure begin!

YOU ARRIVE IN ANCIENT
GREECE

You're in a land steeped in myth and mystery. Your quest is to claim the ultimate prize: the Golden Fleece.

Of course you'll need to be brave but, more importantly, you'll need to keep your wits about you!

IF YOU THINK YOU'RE READY FOR THE CHALLENGE, GO TO PAGE 34

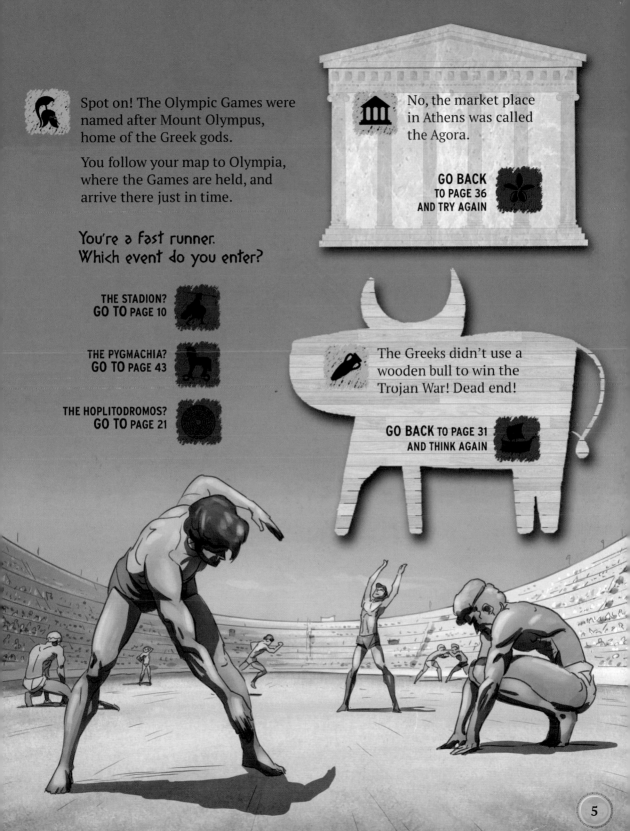

Spot on! The Olympic Games were named after Mount Olympus, home of the Greek gods.

You follow your map to Olympia, where the Games are held, and arrive there just in time.

You're a fast runner. Which event do you enter?

THE STADION?
GO TO PAGE 10

THE PYGMACHIA?
GO TO PAGE 43

THE HOPLITODROMOS?
GO TO PAGE 21

No, the market place in Athens was called the Agora.

GO BACK
TO PAGE 36
AND TRY AGAIN

The Greeks didn't use a wooden bull to win the Trojan War! Dead end!

GO BACK TO PAGE 31
AND THINK AGAIN

5

Yes – you remember the advice of King Cadmus. To kill a dragon, you will need the teeth of a dragon!

As you enter the sacred grove, the dragon charges. You reach into the bag and scatter the teeth. Where each tooth lands, a fully armed warrior springs up. The warriors kill the dragon and then disappear.

The Golden Fleece is yours! Congratulations! You have completed your quest successfully and may now call yourself a true hero of ancient Greece!

 No, Hermes had wings on his heels and was the god of travel and messengers.

GO BACK
TO PAGE 17
AND TRY AGAIN

 Try again! They didn't award medals at the ancient Olympic Games.

GO BACK
TO PAGE 10
AND CHOOSE
AGAIN

 You can hear the hull of your ship splintering as it strikes the jagged rocks hidden beneath the sea!

YOU'VE TAKEN THE
WRONG COURSE –
ROW BACK TO PAGE 14
AND TRY AGAIN

 Argos was famous for horses, not ships.

GO BACK TO
PAGE 23 AND
TRY AGAIN

8

No, Icarus wasn't in the air long enough for his arms to grow weak.

GO BACK TO PAGE 18 AND TRY AGAIN

 It's not in Knossos, on Crete. That's the home of the terrible Minotaur.

GO BACK TO PAGE 35 AND TRY AGAIN

 That's right. Spartan boys were taken from their families at the age of seven and spent years learning fighting skills.

The soldiers look cross that you're doing so well.

"Question three: At the Battle of Thermopylae, a small band of Spartans held back the Persian army of 300,000 men. How many Spartans were there?"

3000.
GO TO PAGE 36

300.
TURN TO PAGE 30

Good choice! The *stadion* was a 200-metre race. You win easily.

What prize do you win?

A GOLD MEDAL.
GO TO PAGE 8

AN OLIVE BRANCH.
GO TO PAGE 39

 Correct, the Minotaur had a bull's head and a man's body.

"I won't make this challenge easy for you. The chart is my prized possession. To find out where the entrance to the maze is, you must answer two questions correctly. Firstly, what was the name of the man who built the maze for me?"

IF YOU THINK IT'S DAEDALUS, **GO TO** PAGE 18

IF ODYSSEUS IS YOUR GUESS, **TURN TO** PAGE 12

 Oops! You scored 86. Your luck is as bad as your maths!

GO BACK TO PAGE 40 AND TRY AGAIN

 No! Doorway B opens onto a steep drop into nothingness!

PULL YOURSELF BACK TO PAGE 28 BEFORE IT'S TOO LATE

The shiny shield is right!

You pick the shield up just as Medusa appears. When she turns to look at you, you hold up the shield so that she can see her own reflection – turning herself to stone!

You cut off her head and carefully put it in a bag to take it with you. Even when she's dead, her gaze can turn living things to stone.

CONTINUE ON YOUR JOURNEY TO ATHENS ON PAGE 36

Bad choice! The *exomis* is worn by a soldier who fights on land. You'll need something warmer at sea.

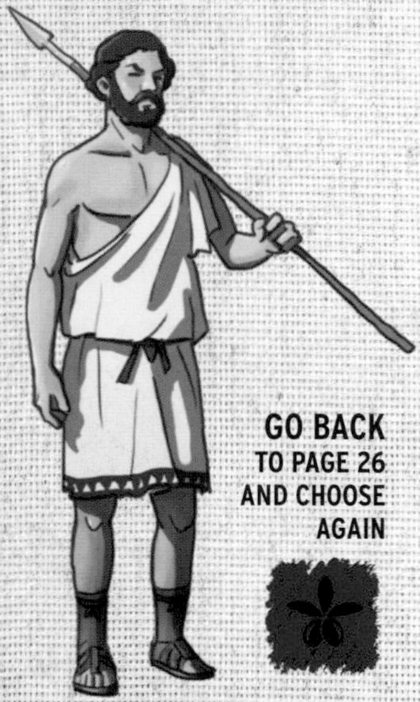

GO BACK TO PAGE 26 AND CHOOSE AGAIN

No, although the shield will provide some protection against the Minotaur, you will never find your way out again.

GO BACK TO PAGE 42 AND TRY AGAIN

Spartan women were just as fierce as their men. "With your shield, or on it" means come back victorious (with your shield) or dead (carried on it).

"Question two: At what age does a Spartan begin his military training?"

Odysseus was a clever Greek hero, but he didn't build the maze.

GO BACK TO PAGE 10 AND TRY AGAIN

SEVEN. FLIP TO PAGE 9

SIXTEEN. GO TO PAGE 20

That's right, pulling on an end would be too easy. Alexander the Great cut the Gordian knot with his sword – so you do the same.

The chest springs open. You grab the chart and just at that moment the Minotaur bursts in!

You run back through the maze, following the thread to the heavy bronze doors.

But they're locked!

TURN TO
PAGE 27
TO REVEAL YOUR FATE

No! Apollo spread plague, gave men donkeys' ears and did many other terrible things to those who defied him, but he didn't turn anyone to stone.

GO BACK
TO PAGE 30
AND THINK AGAIN

That's right! Homer was blind and so spoke his stories aloud. They were later written down by others.

The Minotaur rounds the corner. He's about to spring at you when Minos opens the doors and you escape!

You run to the harbour with the chart and set sail for the treacherous waters that lead to the Black Sea.

The dangerous rocks and whirlpools are marked on the chart, and each is given the name of a goddess.

To come safely through, you must sail left of Love, right of Marriage, right of the Hunt, left of Harvest. Work out what each goddess represents, and choose a course to sail.

APHRODITE

HERA

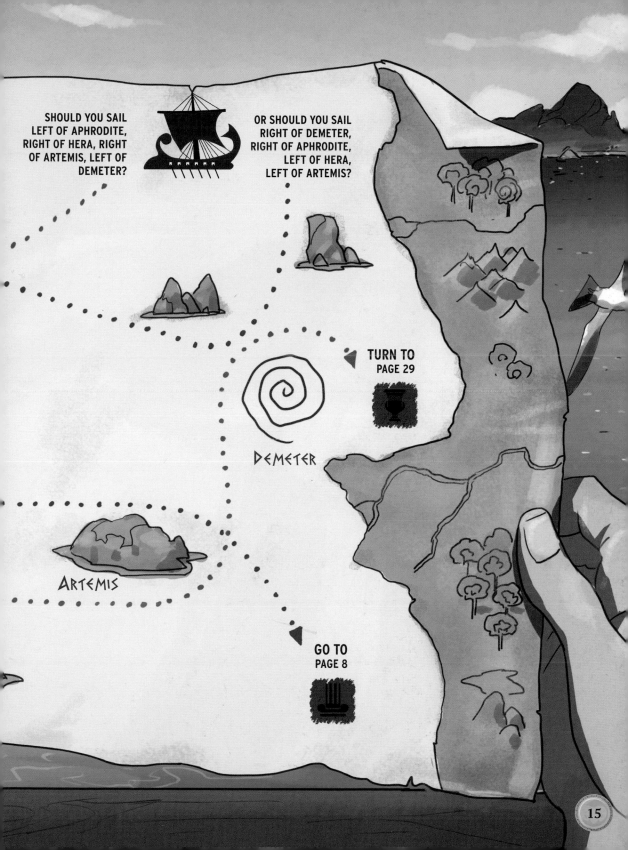

Correct. There were Seven Wonders of the Ancient World, and Cerberus, the gigantic hound that guarded the Underworld, had three heads: 7+3=10, an even number.

The staircase leads you to a chamber in the heart of the maze, but it's locked!

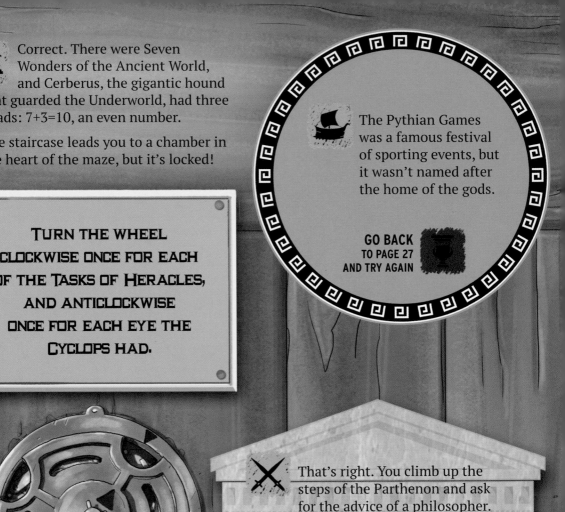

The Pythian Games was a famous festival of sporting events, but it wasn't named after the home of the gods.

GO BACK
TO PAGE 27
AND TRY AGAIN

TURN THE WHEEL CLOCKWISE ONCE FOR EACH OF THE TASKS OF HERACLES, AND ANTICLOCKWISE ONCE FOR EACH EYE THE CYCLOPS HAD.

That's right. You climb up the steps of the Parthenon and ask for the advice of a philosopher.

You will need the protection of the gods on your journey, so choose the ship that is named after the god of the sea.

Do you turn it:

12 TIMES CLOCKWISE AND ONCE ANTICLOCKWISE? **TURN TO PAGE 19**

TWICE CLOCKWISE AND FOUR TIMES ANTICLOCKWISE? **GO TO PAGE 37**

So which ship do you choose?

THE POSEIDON. **GO TO PAGE 28**

THE HADES. **TURN TO PAGE 43**

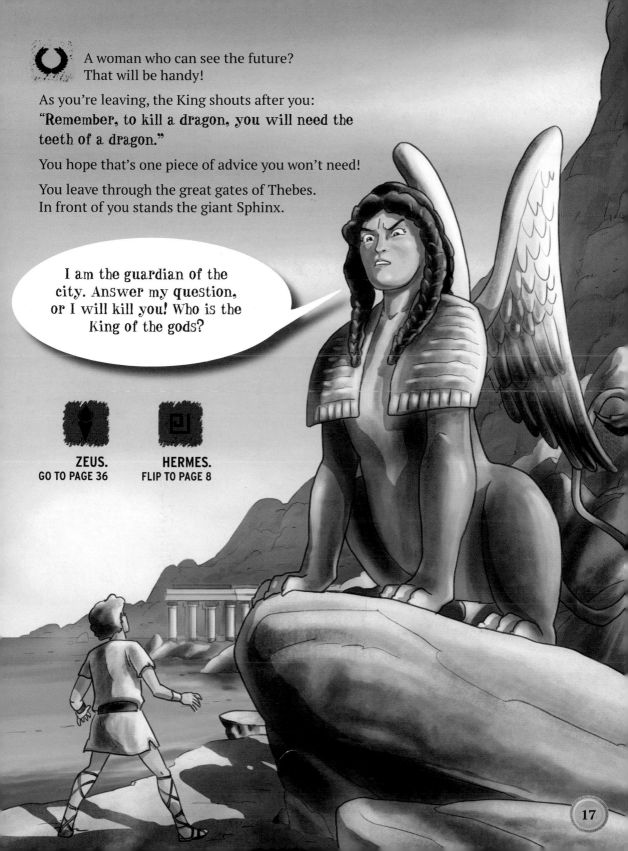

A woman who can see the future? That will be handy!

As you're leaving, the King shouts after you: "Remember, to kill a dragon, you will need the teeth of a dragon."

You hope that's one piece of advice you won't need!

You leave through the great gates of Thebes. In front of you stands the giant Sphinx.

I am the guardian of the city. Answer my question, or I will kill you! Who is the King of the gods?

ZEUS.
GO TO PAGE 36

HERMES.
FLIP TO PAGE 8

Daedalus is right! Minos takes you to the doors that lead to the maze. For the key, you have one more question to answer.

Well done! You've solved the famous Riddle of the Sphinx!

AT THE DAWN OF OUR LIVES, WHEN WE'RE BABIES, WE CRAWL ON FOUR LEGS. AT NOON, WHEN WE'RE GROWN, WE WALK ON TWO LEGS. AT SUNSET, WHEN WE'RE OLD, WE NEED A STICK, WHICH MAKES THREE.

The Sphinx lets you go.

You'll need a ship and crew, but you have no money and no idea where to begin. The King said you should go to the Oracle if you needed help. You'd better head to Delphi.

YOU TRAVEL ACROSS THE LAND TO DELPHI ON PAGE 27

Daedalus had a son called Icarus who stuck feathers to his arms with wax and learned to fly. But he fell to his death because he made a terrible mistake. What did he do?

HE FLEW TOO CLOSE TO THE SUN. **TURN TO** PAGE 42

HE FLEW FOR TOO LONG AND HIS ARMS GOT TIRED. **GO TO** PAGE 9

No, Orpheus was a great musician who travelled into the Underworld to try and bring back Eurydice, the woman he loved.

GO BACK
TO PAGE 41
AND TRY AGAIN

 Try again! The Isthmian and Nemean Games were held every two years, but not the Olympics.

GO BACK
TO PAGE 42
AND CHOOSE AGAIN

 That's right! Heracles had to perform 12 tasks, and the Cyclops only had one eye.

In the chamber is a treasure chest, which contains the chart – but wrapped around the chest is a rope tied in an impossibly complicated knot.

King Gordias tied the most difficult knot in the world. Many people tried (and failed) to undo the knot before Alexander the Great at last succeeded. What did he do?

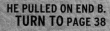 HE PULLED ON END A.
GO TO PAGE 21

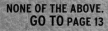 HE PULLED ON END B.
TURN TO PAGE 38

NONE OF THE ABOVE.
GO TO PAGE 13

 A net is no use – Medusa can still look at you.

GO BACK TO PAGE 38
TO CHOOSE ANOTHER WEAPON

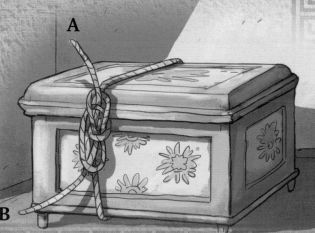

A

B

No, a centaur is half-man, half-horse. Centaurs could be wild beasts or wise teachers.

GO BACK
TO PAGE 32
AND TRY AGAIN

Think again! A sphinx always stands on four legs – that's why you can never outrun them.

GO BACK
TO PAGE 36 AND
TRY AGAIN

Oh no, you were doing so well! By the age of 16, a Spartan boy had been training for nine years.

GO BACK
TO PAGE 12
AND TRY AGAIN QUICKLY!

The Trojan War lasted longer than five years.

GO BACK
TO PAGE 24
AND THINK
AGAIN

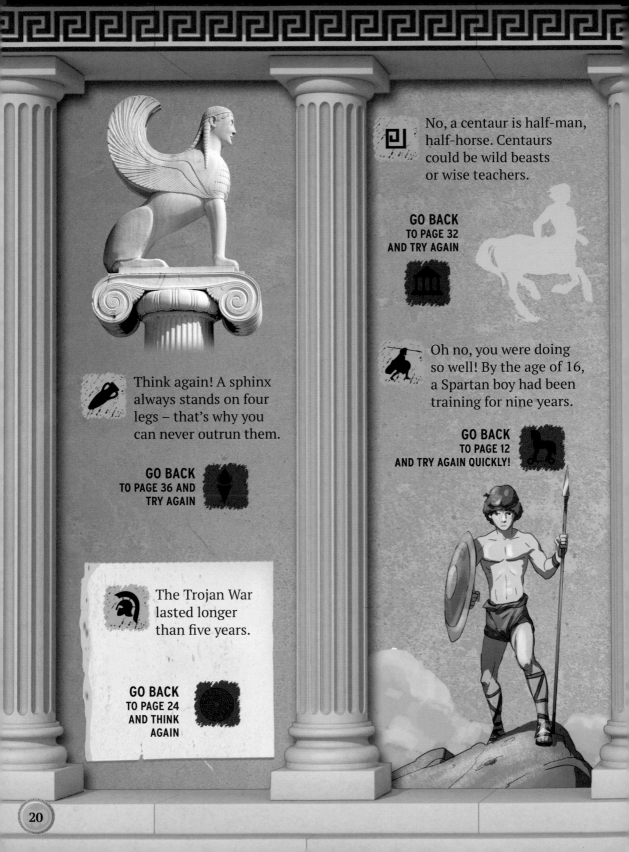

The *hoplitodromos* (running soldier) race was run in full armour on a hot day – it was hard. You'll never win!

GO BACK
TO PAGE 5
AND TRY AGAIN

The help you'll need isn't found in books!

GO BACK
TO PAGE 33
AND TRY AGAIN

Oh dear! Pulling on that end has made it tighter!

GO BACK
TO PAGE 19
AND THINK AGAIN

No! King Midas was known for his greed for gold. The gods punished him by turning everything he touched to gold.

GO BACK
TO PAGE 28
AND TRY AGAIN

Spartans try to look their best just before going into battle. Run faster!

Unfortunately, you're still tired from the Olympics and you can't get away in time.

We won't kill you... if you can answer the three hardest questions we can think of! Question one: What does a Spartan wife say to her husband when he goes off to fight?

"COME BACK WITH YOUR SHIELD, OR ON IT."
TURN TO PAGE 12

"STAND AT THE BACK AND TRY NOT TO GET HURT."
GO TO PAGE 37

"FIGHT BRAVELY AND THEY MIGHT MAKE YOU A GENERAL."
OFF TO PAGE 41

That's right – just like today, the Olympic Games were held once every four years.

Happy, he tells you that the best sailors and ships are to be found in the city that won the Battle of Salamis. But which city was that?

ATHENS?
TURN TO PAGE 39

ARGOS?
JUMP TO PAGE 8

You pull out Medusa's head and point the eyes towards Cetus. The monster shrieks and turns to stone.

You sail on towards Colchis. When you reach land, the witch princess Medea meets you – she knows where the Golden Fleece is.

Medea leads you to the Golden Fleece – the skin of a great, winged, golden ram. You will need to kill the guardian dragon before you can take it. Medea offers you a choice of weapons to defeat the dragon.

Which do you take?

Clue: Remember the advice King Cadmus gave you at the start of your quest.

THE AXE?
TURN TO PAGE 37

THE LANCE?
GO TO PAGE 43

THE BAG OF HUGE TEETH?
HEAD TO PAGE 6

The ball of thread is your secret weapon. You tie one end to the door handle. As you go around the maze, you can let out the thread and then follow it to find your way out.

"Good luck, young hero," says Minos as he closes the doors behind you. They clang heavily and the Minotaur's roar echoes through the maze. You'll have to work fast.

A sign in front of you says:

TAKE ONE PACE FOR EVERY YEAR OF THE TROJAN WAR, THEN TURN RIGHT.

FOR **TEN YEARS**, GO TO PAGE 31

FOR **FIVE YEARS**, TURN TO PAGE 20

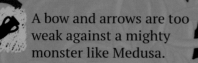

A bow and arrows are too weak against a mighty monster like Medusa.

GO BACK
TO PAGE 38
TO CHOOSE
ANOTHER WEAPON

Wrong move! The staircase on the right collapses and you find yourself hanging over a pit filled with poisonous snakes!

CLIMB BACK UP
TO PAGE 41
AND TRY AGAIN

That's right. You must sail to Colchis on the Black Sea.

The King is impressed. "For your long, hazardous journey, I will give you three things. First, choose an item of clothing."

You are offered three choices, but which is most suitable for an adventure at sea?

HIMATION.
GO TO
PAGE 28

EXOMIS.
GO TO
PAGE 12

TUNIC.
TURN TO
PAGE 41

 When you reach Delphi, you make your way to the temple.

I will help any friend of wise King Cadmus. This is my advice: to be a hero, you must first become a champion. There are four festivals of games here in Greece. You must compete at the one named after the home of the gods.

What is she talking about?

THE ISTHMIAN AND NEMEAN GAMES?
GO TO PAGE 37

THE OLYMPIC GAMES?
TURN TO PAGE 5

THE PYTHIAN GAMES?
FLIP TO PAGE 16

 You bang on the doors.

PASSWORD!
What's the name of the blind poet who told the story of Odysseus?

HOMER.
HEAD TO PAGE 14

SOCRATES.
GO TO PAGE 43

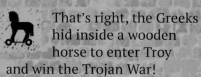

That's right, the Greeks hid inside a wooden horse to enter Troy and win the Trojan War!

You turn left, but the roaring of the Minotaur is nearer now. You need to keep a cool head!

There are two doorways ahead of you. A sign says:

ADD THE NUMBER OF FEET A CENTAUR HAS TO THE NUMBER OF THE MUSES.

For a clue, go to page 33.

IF YOUR ANSWER IS MORE THAN 10, GO THROUGH **DOORWAY A** ON PAGE 41

IF YOUR ANSWER IS LESS THAN 10, GO THROUGH **DOORWAY B** ON PAGE 10

Choose again. The *himation* will keep you warm, but it will restrict your movements when you're fighting and that could cost you your life.

GO BACK TO PAGE 26 AND TRY AGAIN

Poseidon was the god of the sea, so you choose that ship and set sail.

The crew tell you that the journey from the Mediterranean to the Black Sea is dangerous. The only chart showing safe passage belongs to the King of Crete, whose palace is at Knossos.

But what's his name?

KING MIDAS. GO TO PAGE 21

KING MINOS. TURN TO PAGE 32

Correct – Aphrodite was the goddess of love, Hera of marriage, Artemis of the hunt and Demeter the goddess of the harvest.

And you've made it into the Black Sea! Suddenly the waters seem to boil as Cetus, a gigantic sea monster, rears up.

You can't escape, but what have you picked up on your journey that can defeat Cetus?

THE HEAD OF MEDUSA.
TURN TO PAGE 23

THE SPARTAN SWORD.
HEAD TO PAGE 31

Yes, 300 soldiers held off 300,000 – one of the greatest achievements in any battle.

The soldiers decide to give you a chance, so you tell them about your quest. They think you're brave, and give you a Spartan sword to help you on your adventure.

You continue your journey to Athens, but after a few miles, statues of soldiers block your path. You look more closely – they are real soldiers turned to stone!

Who could have done this?

THE MONSTER MEDUSA. **GO TO** PAGE 38

APOLLO, GOD OF THE SUN. **GO TO** PAGE 13

 Calm down. Although he's not happy that you beat him at the race, he's not trying to fight you!

GO BACK TO PAGE 39 BEFORE HE CHANGES HIS MIND!

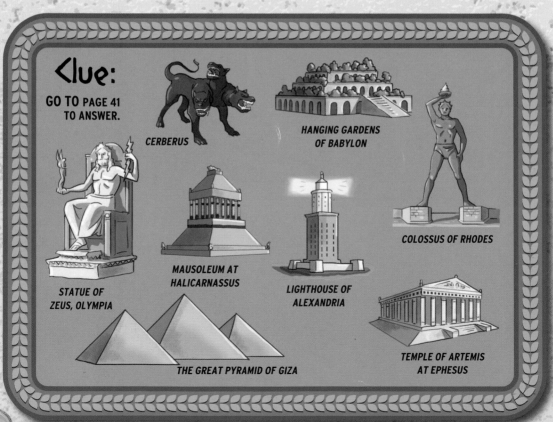

Clue:

GO TO PAGE 41 TO ANSWER.

CERBERUS

HANGING GARDENS OF BABYLON

COLOSSUS OF RHODES

STATUE OF ZEUS, OLYMPIA

MAUSOLEUM AT HALICARNASSUS

LIGHTHOUSE OF ALEXANDRIA

THE GREAT PYRAMID OF GIZA

TEMPLE OF ARTEMIS AT EPHESUS

The Spartan sword would make short work of a man, but against Cetus, it's little better than a toothpick.

GO BACK TO PAGE 29 AND THINK AGAIN

That's right, the Trojan War lasted 10 years. You walk 10 paces and turn right.

In front of you is a doorway – and there's a question on the wall.

Which wooden animal gave the Greeks victory in Troy?

TURN RIGHT FOR THE BULL. OFF TO PAGE 5

TURN LEFT FOR THE HORSE. GO TO PAGE 28

Correct! You arrive in Knossos to a warm welcome (but take care – Minos is not to be trusted).

The chart is in the labyrinth – the large maze beneath my palace. It is guarded by the man-eating Minotaur. If you can get past the beast, you may take the chart.

A man-eating beast! What is the Minotaur?

HALF-MAN, HALF-HORSE.
TURN TO PAGE 20

HALF-MAN, HALF-BULL.
GO TO PAGE 10

The map is yours! It was Jason, with his crew of heroes called Argonauts, who searched for the fleece.

"Finally, some advice," the King says. "Go to the Oracle at Delphi in times of need."

But what is the Oracle?

A WOMAN WHO CAN FORETELL THE FUTURE. **GO TO PAGE 17**

A GREAT BOOK FULL OF ANCIENT LEARNING. **TURN TO PAGE 21**

Muses clue:

The muses were goddesses of the arts and sciences, such as dancing, drama and astronomy. Count them below.

GO TO PAGE 28 TO ANSWER

Greek numbers clue:

1 = α	10 = ι	100 = ρ
2 = β	20 = κ	200 = σ
3 = γ	30 = λ	300 = τ
4 = δ	40 = μ	400 = υ
5 = ε	50 = ν	500 = φ
6 = ς (ϝ)	60 = ξ	600 = χ
7 = ζ	70 = ο	700 = ψ
8 = η	80 = π	800 = ω
9 = θ	90 = ϙ	900 = ϡ

BACK TO PAGE 40 TO ANSWER THE QUESTION

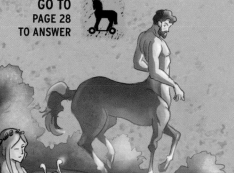

BLACK SEA

COLCHIS

COLCHIS?
FLIP TO
PAGE 26

TROY?
JUMP TO
PAGE 38

TROY

DELPHI
THEBES

SPARTA
ATHENS

KNOSSOS

MEDITERRANEAN SEA

KNOSSOS?
GO TO PAGE 9

At last you arrive in Athens and you are greeted by a crowd of people. You're a great Olympic champion so many fine sailors volunteer to help you in your quest.

The Athenians offer you any ship, but which one do you take?

To help you choose a ship, ask a wise man called a philosopher. You'll find one in the Parthenon.

What is the Parthenon?

A TEMPLE OF THE GODDESS ATHENA. **GO TO** PAGE 16

THE MARKET PLACE. **GO TO** PAGE 5

Correct, Zeus is the King of the gods. But the Sphinx smiles a terrible smile.

"You're a clever one. But if you cannot answer my riddle, I will still kill you. What goes on four legs at dawn, on two legs at noon and on three legs at sunset?"

Believe it or not, 3000 is too many!

GO BACK TO PAGE 9 AND **THINK AGAIN**

A PERSON? GO TO PAGE 18

A SPHINX? GO TO PAGE 20

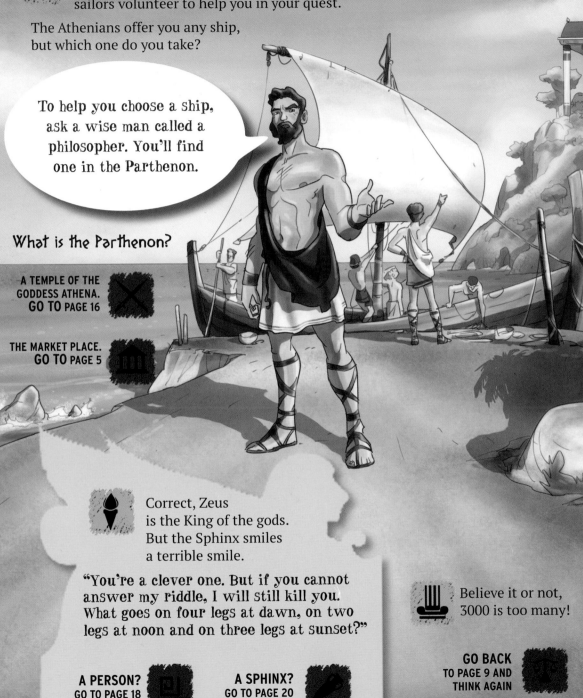

The Isthmian and Nemean Games were famous festivals of sporting events, but they weren't named after the home of the gods.

GO BACK TO PAGE 27 AND TRY AGAIN

No! For starters, the Cyclops didn't have four eyes!

GO BACK TO PAGE 16 AND HAVE ANOTHER GO

Spartans prized bravery above all things. No Spartan would ever avoid danger.

GO BACK TO PAGE 22 AND THINK AGAIN BEFORE THEY KILL YOU!

The axe might just be sharp enough to hurt the dragon, but not to kill it.

TRY TO REMEMBER CADMUS'S ADVICE AND **TRY AGAIN** ON PAGE 23

No, the knot won't budge.

GO BACK TO PAGE 19 AND THINK AGAIN

Correct!

Medusa, a monster with snakes for hair, could turn men to stone just by looking at them.

She's probably nearby, so be prepared to face her. Your Spartan sword is of no use, but there are weapons on the ground.

Which will kill Medusa?

No, it's not in Troy. Troy's greatest treasure was Helen, the most beautiful woman in the world.

GO BACK TO PAGE 35 AND TRY AGAIN

A BOW AND ARROWS?
HEAD TO PAGE 26

A SHINY SHIELD?
TURN TO PAGE 11

A NET?
ON TO PAGE 19

Yes, you're given an olive branch! Olympic champions were celebrated throughout Greece, so you'll easily find a ship and a crew now. But where?

You ask another athlete.

I'll help you, but only after a game of knucklebones.

What game is that?

A FIGHT? **GO TO PAGE 30**

A GAME PLAYED WITH SMALL BONES? **GO TO PAGE 40**

Yes, the Athenians defeated the Persians at the Battle of Salamis.

Next stop: Athens! But your route there takes you through the territory of the sworn enemies of Athens – the Spartans! You pass some Spartan warriors – combing their hair and putting oil and perfume on their bodies.

What do you do?

RUN AWAY. THEY'RE STILL WARRIORS! **SPRINT TO PAGE 22**

POINT AND LAUGH! THEY'RE NOT SO SCARY AFTER ALL. **TURN TO PAGE 42**

The lance is too long to be of any use in the narrow corridors of the maze.

GO BACK TO PAGE 42 AND TRY AGAIN

Correct!

You take turns throwing small bones in the air. Each bone is covered in a few different letters, which represent Greek numbers. You catch each bone on the back of your hand and add up the numbers. The first person to score 100 wins.

Who reaches 100 first?

YOUR CHALLENGER.
GO TO PAGE 42

YOU!
GO TO
PAGE 10

Need to freshen up on your Greek numbers? Go to page 33 for a clue.

The tunic is the best choice. It'll keep you warm and you can move freely in it to fight or sail.

"To keep this map, tell me which hero has already searched for the Golden Fleece?" the King says.

ORPHEUS?
GO TO
PAGE 19

JASON?
JUMP TO
PAGE 33

Unlucky! Spartans weren't interested in being promoted. They prided themselves on being equals in their army.

GO BACK
TO PAGE 22
AND THINK AGAIN

Correct. A centaur has the body of a horse so has four feet and there were nine Muses (goddesses of the arts and sciences): 4+9=13.

You go through Door A. You can hear the Minotaur's footsteps in the corridor!

You run forwards until you reach two spiral staircases.

Add the number of Wonders of the World to the number of heads of the dog Cerberus. If the number is even, go down the staircase on the left. If it's odd, go up the staircase on the right.

For a clue, go to page 30.

THE STAIRCASE ON THE LEFT. **TURN TO** PAGE 16

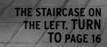

THE STAIRCASE ON THE RIGHT. **GO TO** PAGE 26

That's right. Icarus was warned not to fly too high, but he didn't listen. The sun's heat melted the wax and Icarus fell.

"I will give you a fair chance," the King says. "Take one of these items to help you in the maze."

Which one do you take?

THE SHIELD.
HEAD TO PAGE 12

THE BALL OF THREAD.
TURN TO
PAGE 24

THE LANCE.
GO TO PAGE 39

"Yes, I won," cries the athlete, dancing around. "My score was 105!"

Before you can remind him that you need to get a ship, he asks,

"I still want to be champion of the *stadion*. How long until the next Olympic Games?"

 TWO YEARS.
GO TO
PAGE 19

 FOUR YEARS.
TURN TO
PAGE 23

Never laugh at a Spartan. Honour was important to the most ruthless soldiers in Greece.

STOP AT ONCE.
GO BACK TO
PAGE 39 BEFORE
THEY KILL YOU

42

No, Socrates was a wise philosopher, but he didn't tell stories!

GO BACK TO PAGE 27 – QUICK!

A lance might hold the dragon back for a time, but it won't be able to pierce the dragon's thick scales and kill it.

TRY TO REMEMBER CADMUS'S ADVICE AND GO BACK TO PAGE 23

The *pygmachia* was an event that involved boxing in metal gloves! Even if you win, you'll be black and blue.

GO BACK TO PAGE 5 AND TRY AGAIN

Hades was the god of the Underworld. Not a place you want to go! A three-headed dog called Cerberus guarded the gates to the Underworld.

GO BACK TO PAGE 16 AND CHOOSE ANOTHER SHIP

GLOSSARY

Alexander the Great
Born in 356 BCE, Alexander III of Macedon was one of the greatest leaders ever. He conquered Egypt, Persia and many other lands until his empire stretched all the way from Greece to India. Undefeated in battle, he died aged only 32.

Apollo
Greek god of the Sun, arts, medicine and prophecy.

Argonauts
A crew of 50 sailors who sailed with Jason on his search for the Golden Fleece. They were named after their ship, the *Argo*.

Athena
Goddess of wisdom, and the patron goddess of Athens.

Centaur
A legendary creature that is half-man, half-horse.

Cerberus
A giant dog with three heads.

Cyclops
Mythical giants with only one eye. The great hero Odysseus was captured by a Cyclops, but tricked it and escaped.

God and Goddess
An immortal being believed to have control over something, such as the sea or victory in battle.

Heracles
Also known as Hercules, this legendary hero was famous for his strength. He had to perform 12 almost impossible tasks to become immortal.

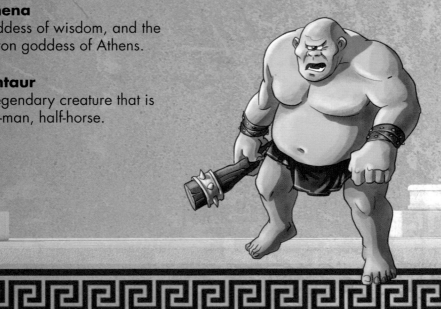

Jason
Legendary hero who led the Argonauts through many adventures in their search for the Golden Fleece.

Labyrinth
A large maze beneath King Minos's palace in Knossos, Crete.

Medea
In Greek legend, a witch princess who helped Jason take the Golden Fleece. In return, he married her.

Medusa
A Gorgon monster with snakes for hair and a gaze that could turn people to stone.

Minotaur
A mythical monster that was half-man, half-bull. It lived in the maze beneath King Minos's palace.

Mycenae
Kingdom ruled by Agamemnon, the most powerful Greek king at the time of the Trojan War.

Olympic Games
The first Olympic Games – a series of athletic competitions – were held in 776 BCE in honour of the Olympian gods.

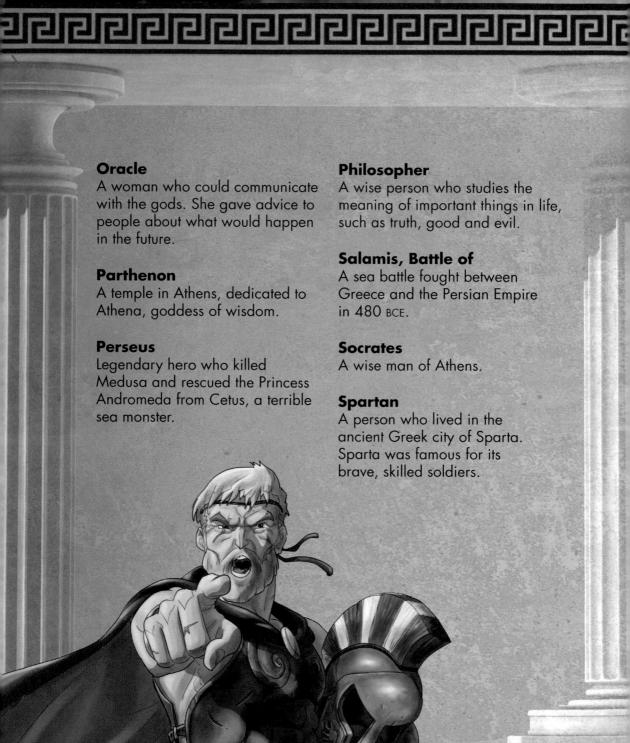

Oracle
A woman who could communicate with the gods. She gave advice to people about what would happen in the future.

Parthenon
A temple in Athens, dedicated to Athena, goddess of wisdom.

Perseus
Legendary hero who killed Medusa and rescued the Princess Andromeda from Cetus, a terrible sea monster.

Philosopher
A wise person who studies the meaning of important things in life, such as truth, good and evil.

Salamis, Battle of
A sea battle fought between Greece and the Persian Empire in 480 BCE.

Socrates
A wise man of Athens.

Spartan
A person who lived in the ancient Greek city of Sparta. Sparta was famous for its brave, skilled soldiers.

Thermopylae, Battle of
A small Greek force held off the much larger Persian army, until they were betrayed.

Trojan War
According to legend, a war fought between the Greeks and the Trojans because the Trojan prince Paris fell in love with the wife of the Greek king. Paris took Helen back with him to Troy.

Underworld
The ancient Greeks believed in a place where spirits of the dead lived. It was also known as Hades.

Sphinx
A legendary creature with the head of a woman and the body of a lion. A sphinx lay at the gates of Thebes and killed people who could not answer her riddles.

Thebes
A city in central Greece, founded by King Cadmus.

Wonders of the World
There were Seven Wonders of the Ancient World: the Great Pyramid of Giza, the Hanging Gardens of Babylon, the Pharos (lighthouse) of Alexandria, the Colossus of Rhodes, the Tomb of King Mausolus in Halicarnassus, the statue of Zeus at Olympia and the temple of Artemis at Ephesus.

TAKING IT FURTHER

The History Quest books are designed to inspire children to develop and apply their historical knowledge through compelling adventure stories. For each story, children must solve a series of historical problems on their way to completing an exciting quest.

The books do not follow a page-by-page order. The reader jumps forwards and backwards through the book according to the answers given to the problems. If their answers are correct, the reader progresses to the next part of the story; incorrect answers are fully explained before the reader is directed back to attempt the problem again. Additional help may be found in the glossary at the back of the book.

To support the development of your child's historical knowledge you can:

- Read the book with your child.

- Continue reading with your child until he or she has understood how to follow the 'Go to' instructions to the next puzzle or explanation, and is flipping through the book confidently.

- Encourage your child to read on alone. Prompt your child to tell you how the story develops and what problems they have solved. Take the time to ask, "What's happening now?"

- Discuss what it would be like if an ancient Greek visited us today. Or if we went back in time to ancient Greece.

- Take advantage of the many sources of historical information – libraries, museums and documentaries. The Internet is another valuable resource, and there is plenty of material specially aimed at children. Take care only to visit websites endorsed by respected educational authorities, such as museums and universities.

- Remember, we learn most when we're enjoying ourselves, so make history fun!